A lot to do

by Jayne Garner

Acknowledgements

Photographs:

Page 6 © NewsCast

Actor: Stephen Illidge

First published in Great Britain by Axis Education Ltd

ISBN 1-903685-63-X

Axis Education
PO Box 459
Shrewsbury
SY4 4WZ

Email: enquiries@axiseducation.co.uk

www.axiseducation.co.uk

Printed by the Cromwell Press

John has a lot to do.

Shall I make a list first?

No, it will take too long.

Shall I go to the shop first?

No, it is too far.

Shall I tidy up first?

No, I do not like that job.

Shall I get dinner first?

No, there is nothing to eat.

Shall I post the letter first?

No, I do not have a stamp.

Shall I wash the dishes first?

No, the water is cold.

Shall I walk the dog first?

No, I can not find his lead.

Shall I cut the grass first?

No, the grass is still wet.

Shall I mop the kitchen floor first?

No, it is best to do that job last.

I am in a muddle. There is a lot to do.

What shall I do first?

I think I had better make a list!